ASK ME ANOTHER

"ASK
ME
ANOTHER"

More Sets of Questions
and Answers
on 36 Different Biblical Subjects

HENRY E. WALTER, LTD.
26 GRAFTON ROAD, WORTHING
and LONDON

FOREWORD

PERHAPS no modern way of making Study of the Scriptures interesting has been devised to equal the Bible Quiz. Far from being a passing fashion, this method has now established itself as one of the most effective ways of building up Group Bible Study.

The present book is the seventh in the very popular series of the " BIBLE QUIZ FAMILY " issued by this firm. The present book however, is essentially different from the six which precede it, as a glance at the contents will show.

Every Quiz in this book is concerned with a pair of Bible Characters closely connected in Scripture with each other. Thus an opportunity is given to learn much about what the WORD OF GOD tells of the groups of people whose activities were generally associated.

The Questions have been designed to give a fairly comprehensive portrait-gallery of the Characters dealt with ; and as instruction as well as interest is the aim of the Quiz, all the questions have the aim of avoiding matter which has no real purpose, but which bear in a practical way on the Subjects dealt with.

As with other Books in this Series, every Quiz can be used with excellent results, in Young People's Gatherings, as well as with Senior Groups. To arrange a competition with one group answering against another, to which marks may be allotted, is a most effective way, not only of creating great interest, but of promoting real enjoyment of the incomparable riches of Holy Scripture.

Henry E. Walter, 1963

First published, January 1963

Published by
HENRY E. WALTER, LTD.,
26 GRAFTON ROAD, WORTHING
and LONDON, W.C.

and Printed by Hedger Godwin & Stewart, Ltd.,
37, New Street, Three Bridges, Crawley, Sussex, England.

CONTENTS

ADAM AND EVE

I.

1. Who planted the Garden of Eden ?
2. Who put Adam in the Garden ?
3. Who gave Adam his name ?
4. What special duty did God give to Adam in the Garden ?
5. What did he give to the animals and the birds ?
6. Which tree in the Garden was forbidden to be touched ?
7. And what would be the penalty of disobedience ?
8. Why was Eve created ?

II.

9. Why was she called Eve, and who gave her the name ?
10. What is the first question in the Bible, and who asked it ?
11. Did the Serpent first tempt Adam ?
12. What did Eve reply to the Serpent's temptation ?
13. What three reasons made Eve take of the forbidden fruit ?
14. Whom did Adam and Eve hear walking in the Garden ?
15. What is the second question in the Bible, and who asked it ?
16. What was Adam's excuse to God for his disobedience ?

III.

17. What did God make for Adam and Eve ?
18. How did God punish their disobedience ?
19. What was the name of Adam's eldest son ?
20. Give the name of Eve's second son ?
21. The first man, Paul tells us, was Adam, whom does he call the second man ?
22. "As in Adam"—can you finish Paul's sentence ?
23. Adam's seventh descendant, was a prophet. What was his name ?
24. In what other part of the Bible do we read of the Tree of life ?

CAIN AND ABEL

I.

1. What was the name of the first Baby in the Bible?
2. What did his Mother say when he was born?
3. What kind of work did Cain do when he grew up?
4. What offering did Cain bring to God?
5. Did God accept Cain's offering?
6. What three questions did God then ask Cain?
7. What effect did his rejected sacrifice have on Cain?
8. And then what happened between the brothers?

II.

9. Name Adam and Eve's second child?
10. When he grew up, what did he become?
11. What did Abel offer to the Lord?
12. Did God accept or refuse Abel's offering?
13. A New Testament writer gives us a hint why one brother's sacrifice was accepted and the other refused. Do you know why?
14. What further questions did God ask Cain?
15. And what was Cain's answer?
16. What does the Apostle John call Cain?

III.

17. What punishment did God inflict on Cain for his crime?
18. What was Cain's request to God?
19. What did God do in response?
20. What mention does our Lord make of Abel?
21. What parable does a New Testament writer draw between Cain and Abel?
22. What commandment did Cain break?
23. "Whosoever hateth his brothers . . . . . . " Can you complete?
24. What is the last we hear of Cain?

ABRAHAM AND SARAH

I.

1. Both of these characters had their names changed. Why and when ?
2. Why did Abraham leave his native birth place ?
3. Where did Abraham come from, and to what country did he go ?
4. Four relatives started out from Ur. How many reached Canaan ?
5. Soon after reaching their destination, there came a famine. What did the pilgrims then do ?
6. What caused Uncle and Nephew to part company ?
7. Can you name some of the places Abraham lived at while in Canaan ?
8. What special promise was given to Abraham, after Lot left him ?

II.

9. How many armed servants were in Abraham's household ?
10. What did Abraham do when he heard Lot had been captured ?
11. What remarkable person blessed Abraham ?
12. " Be thou perfect." How old was Abraham when God said this to him ?
13. Did Sarah accompany her husband into Palestine ?
14. " She is my sister." How often did Abraham say this of Sarah and why ?
15. How often do we read that Sarah " laughed." When and why ?
16. We also read Abraham " laughed." On what occasion ?

III.

17. How old was Abraham when Isaac was born ?
18. To whom was said " Is anything too hard for the Lord?"
19. Sarah, hidden behind a tent door, heard something to her advantage, why ?
20. What does the Apostle Peter say about Sarah ?
21. Two women are named among the heroes of Faith in Hebrews II. Who are they ?
22. Who did Jesus call "a Son of Abraham?"
23. What was Abraham called by the Apostle James ?
24. " It was not written for his sake alone." Whose sake and who said this ?

HAGAR AND ISHMAEL

I.

1. Of what race was Hagar ?
2. Why did she first run away from Abraham's household ?
3. Who spoke to her as she was wandering in the wilderness ?
4. What did the Angel then fortell her ?
5. What special name did Hagar give to the place where she met the Angel ?
6. What was the name of her baby Son ?
7. Abraham offered a special prayer for Ishmael. What was it ?
8. What was God's answer to this prayer ?

II.

9. To celebrate Isaac's birth, Abraham gave a feast. What did Ishmael do ?
10. And what did this cause Sarah to try and do ?
11. Did Sarah's attitude about this please Abraham ?
12. What course did God then direct Abraham to take ?
13. On the next morning what did Abraham do ?
14. Who accompanied Hagar on her second journey ?
15. In what Wilderness did she wander ?
16. What caused her to despair, and what did she then do ?

III.

17. Where did she leave Ishmael lying by himslef and why ?
18. Whose voice did God hear, Hagar's or Ishmael's ?
19. And what was the Angel's answer, and to whom ?
20. Then God did something to Hagar—what ?
21. What did the Mother do then ?
22. Paul likens Hagar to something very strange, to what ?
23. The same Apostle draws a lesson from Isaac and Ishmael. What ?
24. What is the last we hear of Ishmael ?

LOT AND LABAN

I.

1. Who was the father of Lot?
2. Name the Nephew and Uncle who left Ur of the Chaldees for Palestine?
3. What caused a division between the two?
4. How was this settled?
5. Towards what city did Lot then go?
6. What misfortune soon overtook Lot, and who rescued him?
7. What tragedy later overtook Sodom, and why?
8. How many of the family escaped?

II.

9. Our Lord made two references to Lot. Do you know them?
10. What character does the Apostle Peter give Lot?
11. What happened to Lot's wife?
12. Why did the two angels visit Lot? What message did they bring him?
13. When do we first hear of Laban?
14. Where was Laban and his family living when Abraham's servant visited them?
15. What did Laban say when he saw his visitor at the door?
16. And what was the object of the visit?

III.

17. Later on, a Mother advised her Son to run away to Laban. Name both.
18. How did the Uncle receive his Nephew?
19. To whom did Laban say "Tell me, what shall thy wages be?"
20. What was Laban's excuse when he tricked Jacob about Rachel?
21. Why did Laban specially want Jacob to continue to work for him?
22. How many times did he change Jacob's rate of wages?
23. What two names were given to the heap of stones raised as a witness between Laban and his Nephew?
24. What is the last we hear of Laban?

ISAAC AND REBEKAH

I.

1. Who gave Isaac his name before he was born?
2. What strange command did God give Abraham about Isaac?
3. To what mountain did the Father take his Son?
4. And what was the outcome of his command?
5. Why did Abraham send his Steward to Rebekah's home?
6. Where are we first introduced to Rebekah?
7. What did she decide to do in answer to the steward's request?
8. Where did she see her future Husband?

II.

9. And what did she then immediately do?
10. How did Isaac await his future Bride?
11. What were three of Isaac's principal occupations?
12. Was Isaac successful as a farmer? We are specially told the reason.
13. Why did his enemies come and desire to make a treaty with Isaac?
14. What were the names of his Sons?
15. Do you know the name of Rebekah's Nurse?
16. Growing old, what did Isaac ask Esau specially to get for him?

III.

17. Yet in the end, who received the blessing from Isaac?
18. Why did the younger son leave him?
19. How long did his mother expect him to be away from home?
20. Did he ever see his Father again?
21. Were the two brothers ever reconciled?
22. Who used the words " our Father Isaac?"
23. Our Lord made two references to Isaac, what were they?
24. " In Isaac shall thy seed be called." This occurs three times in the Bible, where?

ESAU AND JACOB

I.

1. What were the characters and pursuits of the twins ?
2. Father and Mother each had a favourite. Which was loved most by which ?
3. For what did Esau sell his birthright ?
4. What request did Isaac when old, make of Esau ?
5. Who overheard the request, and what followed ?
6. What disguise did Jacob assume to deceive his father ?
7. Who suggested all this deception to him ?
8. And what did Jacob obtain by all this trickery ?

II.

9. What happened, when Esau returned ?
10. What caused Jacob to leave home ?
11. There was an additional reason for his going away, what was it ?
12. What momentous interview took place at Jacob's Well ?
13. What does the writer of the Hebrews call Esau ?
14. Where did Jacob have his famous dream, and what was it ?
15. How long did Jacob stay away from home in exile ?
16. What promise did God give Jacob ?

III.

17. How many times do we read " Jacob met the angels of God?"
18. Jacob had an encounter with a mysterious " Man." What do you know about it ?
19. How did Jacob get a new name, and what was it ?
20. How many sons had Jacob ? Do you know any of their names ?
21. Which sons were Jacob's favourites ?
22. When Jacob prayed in his old age, " Bless the lads," to whom did he refer ?
23. Jacob's sons were the ancestors of what famous nation ?
24. What King did Jacob bless shortly before his death ?

JOSEPH AND BENJAMIN

I.

1. Who was Joseph's mother?
2. His father once divided the whole family into a procession. Where was Joseph's place?
3. How old was Joseph when his father sent him out to keep sheep?
4. Who was Jacob's favourite son?
5. How was this favouritism shown?
6. What did the rest of his brothers think of this?
7. Joseph dreamed two dreams. Can you tell what they were?
8. Can you give any meaning to these dreams?

II.

9. What special errand did his father send him on, and to where?
10. Not finding them there, where was he then sent, and by whom?
11. Which of his brothers saved Jacob from being murdered?
12. What did they do to him instead?
13. Whose idea was it to sell Joseph as a slave and to whom?
14. To whom was Joseph next sold?
15. How did he get on in his new position?
16. What two dreams did Joseph interpret whilst in prison?

III.

17. How did Joseph come to be the Prime Minister of Egypt?
18. Why were the brothers ordered to take Benjamin to Egypt?
19. Was his father willing to let him go and for what reason?
20. How did Joseph act when he saw Benjamin once more?
21. In what way did Joseph further show his pleasure at seeing Benjamin?
22. Did both Joseph and Benjamin give their names to any tribes of Israel?
23. In his final blessing, to what animal did Jacob compare Benjamin?
24. What New Testament character speaks of Joseph?

MOSES AND AARON
I.

1. Who was Moses' and Aaron's sister?
2. There was one thing which Aaron could do very well. What was it?
3. What was the outstanding quality of Moses?
4. What caused Moses to run away from Egypt?
5. When did Aaron rejoin his brother?
6. What was the first thing they did together then?
7. And what was the brothers' request of Pharaoh?
8. In what circumstances was Aaron called a prophet, and by whom?

II.

9. Which was the older of the two brothers, and by how much?
10. Aaron had a rod which possessed marvellous powers.
11. What happened when Aaron stretched out his hand over the waters of Egypt?
12. For what reason did Pharaoh call for Moses and Aaron by night?
13. What was the occasion of the Israelites first murmuring against Moses and Aaron?
14. And what was the brothers answer to this?
15. When did Aaron, Moses and one other go up to the top of a hill and what happened?
16. Did both brothers go up into the Mount Sinai to receive the Law?

III.

17. But when Aaron later, was left below, in charge of the people, what happened?
18. What feeble excuse did Aaron offer Moses?
19. To what special position was Aaron and his sons appointed?
20. With what brother was the Lord " very angry," and how was he forgiven?
21. Both brothers died on a mountain. What do you know of the details?
22. Moses was also spoken of as a prophet and by whom?
23. Who is said to have been " faithful in all his house " and by whom?
24. How is an action of Moses compared with our Lord's Crucifixion?

PHARAOH AND JETHRO

I.

1. What child did Pharaoh's daughter bring up as her own son ?
2. What caused Pharaoh to seek to kill Moses ?
3. Do we read of more than one Pharaoh in the book of Exodus ?
4. Why was it safe for Moses to return to Egypt ?
5. What was Pharaoh's first answer to Moses and Aaron's visit ?
6. And what further decree did the King of Egypt issue ?
7. How many plagues fell upon the Egyptians ? How many can you name ?
8. What was the last and most severe visitation on the Egyptians ?

II.

9. What happened when Pharaoh heard the Israelites had fled ?
10. What was the reaction of the Israelites when they saw the Egyptians pursuing them ?
11. How far did the Egyptians pursue the fleeing Israelites ?
12. What calamity overtook the Egyptian army ?
13. Jethro is also called by another name. What is it ?
14. What was the occasion of Moses' first meeting with Jethro ?
15. How many daughters had Jethro ?
16. Three well known Old Testament characters found their wives under similar circumstances ?

III.

17. What was Moses' employment when in exile ?
18. And how long did he stay there ?
19. Besides being a farmer, what else was Jethro ?
20. When Moses wished to return to Egypt, what did Jethro say ?
21. When Jethro heard that Moses had led the Israelites out of Egypt what did he do ?
22. What piece of advice did Jethro give his son-in-law ?
23. Which is the last reference to Moses father-in-law ?
24. Paul gives the reason why Pharaoh was raised up. Why ?

JOSHUA AND CALEB
I.
1. When do we first read of Joshua ?
2. Twice we read of "Moses' minister." Who was he and on what occasion were these references ?
3. When did Joshua say, and to whom :—"There is a noise of war in the camp"?
4. "He departed not out of the Tabernacle." Of whom is this said ?
5. With eleven others Joshua was sent on what special journey ?
6. What other well known man accompanied him ?
7. How many of those who left Egypt actually entered Canaan ?
8. Why were these two allowed this honour ?

II.
9. What description did the Lord give of Joshua to Moses ?
10. What two men were commanded to divide the land of Canaan as soon as the Israelites reached it ?
11. Who was Moses twice told to encourage ?
12. Moses laid his hands on Joshua and with what results ?
13. "Be strong and of a good courage." Twice this was said to Joshua, by whom ?
14. What was Joshua's first act on reaching the borders of Canaan ?
15. What did Joshua command to be taken out of the River Jordan ?
16. What strange encounter did Joshua have outside Jericho ?

III.
17. Forty five years afterwards Caleb claimed his promised inheritance. What place ?
18. What special gift did Caleb's daughter request of him ?
19. How many times did Joshua tell his army to march round Jericho ?
20. Outside what city was Joshua's army defeated ?
21. What did Joshua once command to stand still ?
22. Had the whole of Canaan been subdued before Joshua's death ?
23. How was the land of Canaan finally divided by Joshua ?
24. What famous declaration did Joshua make in his last speech to the people ?

GIDEON AND SAMSON

I.

1. What foreign race had invaded Israel in Gideon's time ?
2. How long did this invasion last ?
3. And what did the Israelites do ?
4. To whom and where did an Angel of the Lord appear ?
5. What was Gideon doing at this time, and where was he ?
6. What was the Angel's greeting to Gideon ?
7. And what was the Angel's further message ?
8. What did Gideon do next ?

II.

9. What strange occurrence then took place, and what conversation followed ?
10. What first command of the Angel did Gideon carry out ?
11. To what small numbers was Gideon's Army of 32,000 reduced and how ?
12. With what weapon did Gideon's men attack the Midianites ?
13. What were the names of Samson's father and mother ?
14. Who announced the coming birth of Samson to his mother ?
15. What did the young Samson do when a lion roared against him ?
16. What do you know about Samson's riddle and its solution ?

III.

17. What adventure did Samson have with 300 foxes ?
18. Samson was caught and shut up in a city. How did he escape ?
19. What woman was the downfall of Samson ?
20. How was he finally taken captive ?
21. What was his final adventure ?
22. What was the great characteristic of Samson ?
23. In what other part of the Bible do we read of Samson ?
24. And in what New Testament book do we read of Gideon ?

RUTH AND NAOMI

I.

1. One book in the Bible is called by a woman's name?
2. In what country was Ruth born?
3. Do you know the name of Ruth's mother-in-law?
4. Why did Ruth and Naomi leave Moab?
5. Did both of Naomi's daughters-in-law accompany her?
6. Naomi asked Ruth to return back. What was her answer?
7. To what town in Israel did they come?
8. At what time of year did they arrive back home?

II.

9. What was the first request Ruth made of Naomi?
10. Into whose fields did Ruth go to glean?
11. What did the farmer say to Ruth?
12. How did Boaz make sure Ruth gathered sufficient?
13. What present did Boaz give Ruth to take back to Naomi?
14. Boaz took off his shoe and gave it to his neighbour. Why did he do this?
15. Why did he purchase Naomi's field?
16. Who did Ruth marry?

III.

17. Who nursed the child born to Ruth?
18. What was the child called?
19. And what celebrated King was this infant's grandson?
20. What Evangelist mentions Ruth?
21. Who said "Entreat me not to leave thee" and to whom?
22. Who was Orpah?
23. What was Naomi's reply to her welcome back to Bethlehem?
24. To whom was it said "The Lord recompense thy work" and by whom?

HANNAH AND ELI

I.

1. Who was Hannah's husband ?
2. What special journey did he make each year ?
3. Do you know the names of Eli's two sons ?
4. What was Hannah's first meeting with Eli ?
5. Hannah prayed very earnestly for—what ?
6. How did Eli come to misunderstand Hannah ?
7. Where did Hannah and her husband live ?
8. What was the name of Hannah's child ?

II.

9. In what special way did she dedicate her child to God ?
10. Do you know any phrases from Hannah's prayer on this occasion ?
11. Did she take her son back with her when she returned home ?
12. What was the child's occupation ?
13. What present did Hannah bring her little son each year ?
14. Of what two children do we read that they were in favour with God and man ?
15. For what reason did a prophet fortell evil news to Eli ?
16. What happened when Eli lay down to sleep one evening?

III.

17. When Samuel heard a voice ; what did he first do ?
18. How many times did the Lord call Samuel ?
19. We read " Eli perceived." What did he perceive ?
20. What did Eli instruct Samuel to answer ?
21. What was the message Samuel was to pass on to Eli ?
22. What did Samuel do then ?
23. And what was Eli's reply when he received the mesage ?
24. How old was Eli when he died and what was the cause of his death ?

SAUL AND JONATHAN

I.

1. When do we first read of Jonahtan ?
2. On one occasion in the whole of Israel's army only two had weapons, who were they ?
3. What secret adventure did Jonathan undertake ?
4. When was Jonathan in danger of being put to death because he ate honey ?
5. How was it this sentence was not carried out ?
6. Who was the tallest King of Israel ?
7. And who was the first King of Israel ?
8. Who found Saul's armour to big for him ?

II.

9. When did Jonathan first meet David, and what then happened ?
10. What caused Saul's daughter to deceive him by means of a bolster ?
11. Who was Jonathan's greatest friend ?
12. On how many occasions did Saul cast javelins at people?
13. On what occasion did Jonathan shoot three arrows ?
14. How many times did David save Saul's life ?
15. When did Saul ask David's pardon ?
16. What caused Saul to consult a witch ?

III.

17. What was the message then given him ?
18. In what battle were Saul and Jonathan killed ?
19. They were " lovely and pleasant in their lives." Who ?
20. Who was Saul's father ?
21. Who said " I have played the fool "?
22. With whom did Jonathan make a covenant ?
23. And who said " I was not disobedient "?
24. What New Testament Apostle bore the same names as Israel's King ?

DAVID AND ABSALOM

I.

1. What relation was Absalom to David ?
2. What was Absalom praised for in all Israel ?
3. How frequently did Absalom have his hair cut ?
4. How long did Absalom live in the same city as David ?
5. What steps did Absalom employ to see David ?
6. What special retinue did Absalom provide for himself ?
7. What did Absalom do to secure popularity ?
8. With what result ?

II.

9. What lying excuse did Absalom give David to explain his absence ?
10. What did the traitor do next ?
11. And what was David's reaction to the rebellion ?
12. What river did David's party cross, in their flight ?
13. What principal councillor of David's joined the conspirator ?
14. Who cast stones at David and cursed him ?
15. What was Ahithophel's counsel to Absalom ?
16. Who suggested pulilng a town into the river with ropes ?

III.

17. What special instructions did David give to his commander ?
18. Where did the battle take place between Absalom's and David's armies ?
19. In what strange way was Absalom prevented from escaping ?
20. How did Joab learn of Absalom's whereabouts ?
21. What was the end of Absalom ?
22. Two men ran a race, who won and why did they run ?
23. What was the King's first question to the mesesngers ?
24. And what was David's cry in answer ?

SOLOMON AND HIRAM

I.

1. Who was Hiram?
2. What materials did he send David and for what purpose?
3. When Hiram heard of Solomon's accession what did he do?
4. What did Solomon propose to carry out David's wish?
5. How were all the materials transported from Tyre to Jerusalem?
6. What did Solomon give Hiram in return?
7. Whose builders prepared the stone and timber to build the Temple?
8. How many years elapsed between the Exodus from Egypt and the commencement of Solomon's Temple?

II.

9. How long did Solomon take to build the Temple?
10. Who was Hiram's father? The Bible gives him a thumb-nail biography?
11. Hiram cast two special bronze pillars, what were they called?
12. What were the contents of the Ark placed in the Temple?
13. In Solomon's prayer at the dedication of the Temple, one phrase occurs 8 times. Do you know the phrase?
14. How many times did God appear to Solomon?
15. What special kind of wood did Hiram supply for building the Temple?
16. Who was the first King of Israel to have a navy?

III.

17. What well known Queen visited Solomon?
18. Why did she pay this visit?
19. We read ' Hiram was ever a lover of '—who?
20. From what country did Solomon import horses?
21. How many chariots had Solomon?
22. What did Solomon choose when asked by God, " What shall I give thee?"
23. Who was Solomon's mother?
24. How many times do we read that God gave Solomon wisdom?

JEROBOAM AND AHIJAH

I.

1. What was the name of Jeroboam's father?
2. As the King saw Jeroboam was industrious, how did he reward him?
3. Going for a walk in a new suit, Jeroboam met a prophet, and what happened?
4. When the King heard of this, what did he do?
5. Where did Jeroboam flee for safety?
6. How did he come to return to Israel?
7. And as soon as he got back what honour did he receive?
8. How many tribes of Israel rebelled, and followed Jeroboam?

II.

9. What made Jeroboam fear that the Ten Tribes would return to the Kingdom of Judah?
10. What means did he take to obviate this?
11. Where were the two Golden Calves set up?
12. What was the result to the people of the Idolatory Jeroboam set up?
13. An unknown prophet foretold the coming of what King, who would restore the worship of God?
14. And what sign did he give in proof of this?
15. What happened to Jeroboam when he sought to arrest this bold prophet?
16. How was the King healed?

III.

17. Did the prophet accept Jeroboam's invitation to come home to dinner?
18. Do you know anything of the singular adventure which then overtook the prophet?
19. What was the name of Jeroboam's son?
20. To whom did the King send to learn whether his son should recover?
21. How did Ahijah recognise the mother when she arrived?
22. How did Ahijah greet her on her entrance?
23. What verdict did he then tell the child's mother?
24. What good character did Ahijah give the child?

AHAB AND JEZEBEL

I.

1. Over what country was Ahab King?
2. What character does the Book of Kings I, give him?
3. Who was his wife?
4. What idol worship did she introduce into Israel?
5. What great calamity fell upon this nation in his reign?
6. And for how long did this last?
7. What threat did Jezebel make to Elijah and why?
8. Who had a possession greatly coveted by Ahab?

II.

9. What was this possession and where was it?
10. How did the King first approach its owner?
11. And what answer was given to him?
12. How did this answer please Ahab?
13. Then Jezebel his wife intervened, by saying?
14. And what advice did she give Ahab?
15. Do you know of her plan to obtain the possession?
16. And what was the outcome of her plot?

III.

17. As soon as the news reached the Queen what did she do?
18. Who was at the entrance of the vineyard to meet Ahab?
19. When the King saw Elijah what did he say?
20. What terrible prediction did the prophet utter?
21. Did this sentence have any effect on Ahab?
22. When did two Kings listen to two prophets before a battle?
23. Why did Ahab change clothes with the King of Judah?
24. Was this ruse successful?

ELIJAH AND OBADIAH

I.

1. Who was Obadiah?
2. How many prophets of the Lord did he save the lives of, and by what means?
3. On what special errand did Ahab send Obadiah?
4. On his way what celebrated Prophet did he meet?
5. What did Elijah tell him to do?
6. Why was Obadiah not anxious to do Elijah's bidding?
7. How did Elijah reassure him?
8. How long did the famine last in Israel?

II.

9. When King and Prophet met, what passed between them?
10. Now Elijah command the King to do—what?
11. On what mountain was this assembly to be held?
12. What question did Elijah put to the Israelites there gathered?
13. And what was their immediate response?
14. What menu did an Angel prepare for Elijah's meal?
15. When do we first hear of Elijah?
16. Whom did Elijah appoint as his successor?

III.

17. After seeing the marvellous happenings, what did the people then say?
18. By the side of which brook did Elijah hide?
19. From there he went to another village, where?
20. With whom did he live while there?
21. What two miracles took place while he lived there?
22. What did the Angel of the Lord command Elijah to do when he came the second time?
23. Who went with Elijah on his last journey?
24. How was Elijah conveyed to Heaven?

ASA AND JOSIAH

I.

1. Was Asa a bad or good King?
2. What did he do to his mother's idol?
3. Who said "O Lord we rest on Thee" and on what occasion?
4. What prophet said to Asa "your work shall be rewarded"?
5. And what was Asa's and the nation's response?
6. How many years did he reign?
7. Josiah's reign was prophesised of by whom, before his birth?
8. How old was he when he was made King?

II.

9. Tell what you know of his character?
10. How long did he reign?
11. What happened when he was 16.
12. Two years later what great work did he begin?
13. During this work what did Hilkiah the priest find?
14. What was done with this find?
15. What was Josiah's reaction on hearing the contents of the book?
16. What answer did Huldah the prophetess give to the King?

III.

17. In the 18th year of Josiah's reign there was held the greatest———ever held in Judah or Israel?
18. What is the Bible's verdict on Josiah?
19. How did Josiah become entangled in the war which led to his death?
20. Which prophet lamented for Josiah?
21. During his reign who was a great prophet?
22. Another Biblical prophet foretold in Josiah's reign?
23. Did the nation follow the Lord in Josiah's day?
24. What did his subjects think of this good King's death?

ESTHER AND MORDECAI

I.

1. One book in the Bible does not contain the word "God." which ?
2. In what book of the Bible is India mentioned ?
3. Who was the King whose history is told in Esther ?
4. How many provinces was there in this great kingdom ?
5. What was the name of his Queen ?
6. When the King commanded her to attend his feast, what did she do ?
7. And what was the result of her refusal ?
8. What was the name of the palace in which the King lived ?

II.

9. When her father and mother were dead, by whom was Esther brought up ?
10. Who did the King appoint Queen after Vashti's punishment ?
11. How did Mordecai happen to save the King's life ?
12. All men, except one, bowed to Haman as the King commanded. Who refused ?
13. What revenge did Haman contemplate ?
14. How did he proceed with his plot ?
15. As soon as Mordecai heard of the plot what did he do ?
16. " If I perish, I perish " who said this and why ?

III.

17. What request did she make of the King ?
18. For what purpose did Haman erect a gallows ?
19. What happened at the Queen's banquet ?
20. And what was the sequel for Haman ?
21. How did Esther secure the cancellation of the slaughter of the Jews ?
22. Which is the longest text in the Bible ?
23. Twice we read of letters being sent by post. Do you know of them ?
24. What single honour did the King confer on Mordecai ?

HEZEKIAH AND ISAIAH

I.

1. Who was Hezekiah's father?
2. How old was he when he came to the throne?
3. And for how long did he reign?
4. What happened to the brazen serpent which Moses had set up in the wilderness centuries before?
5. What did he do in the first year of his reign?
6. How long did it take to cleanse the house of the Lord?
7. What was remarkable about this reformation?
8. What proclamation did Hezekiah send by post?

II.

9. And how was the proclamation received by many?
10. "The good Lord pardon every one." Who prayed this?
11. What invader from Assyria came to besiege Jerusalem?
12. What first precaution did Hezekiah take to beat his enemy?
13. What was Hezekiah's courageous message to his people?
14. What means did the invading army take to break the Jews' spirit?
15. These efforts failing, what further did the Asyrians do?
16. What did the Jews' leaders implore the Assyrians not to do and why?

III.

17. Who was the emissary of the Assyrians?
18. What did Hezekiah do with the Assyrian ultimatum?
19. What great prophet was living in Jerusalem at the time?
20. How did he convey God's answer to Hezekiah?
21. What dramatic event happened to the invading Assyrian army?
22. When the King was dangerously ill, what message did Isaiah bring to him?
23. In answer to the King's prayer, what was Isaiah commissioned to tell him?
24. How was the King healed and what was the sign of his recovery?

EZRA AND NEHEMIAH

I.

1. What heathen King decreed the rebuilding of the Temple at Jerusalem ?
2. What proportion of the Jews wished to return from their exile in Persia ?
3. When the foundations for rebuilding were laid, why was weeping heard as well as joy ?
4. What caused the work of rebuilding of city and temple to cease ?
5. Fourteen years later the work was recommenced under the leadership of what two Jewish leaders ?
6. What was Ezra by profession ?
7. How had he prepared himself to return to Jerusalem ?
8. What King gave Ezra a letter to confirm his return to Jerusalem ?

II.

9. Why did not Ezra ask the King for a military escort to guard their journey through the desert ?
10. How were the returning party of Jews protected on their journey ?
11. On what occasion did a congregation sit in the street in the rain ?
12. What was Nehemiah's occupation ?
13. What caused him such sorrow of heart ?
14. Did the King notice his sadness of mind ?
15. What request did Nehemiah then make of the King ?
16. And what was the King's reply ?

III.

17. How did he first survey the ruins of Jerusalem ?
18. What did he then say to the people about rebuilding the city ?
19. Who was one of Nehemiah's principal opponents ?
20. Why were the builders of the wall armed during their work ?
21. Why were the builders to be on the alert for a trumpet to sound ?
22. Why did Nehemiah have 150 people to dinner each day?
23. What scribe occupied a wooden pulpit for a half-a-day's service ?
24. Who said " The joy of the Lord is your strength "?

NEBUCHADNEZZAR AND BELSHAZZAR

I.

1. When do we first hear of Nebuchadnezzar ?
2. What King of Judah with the Royal Family were taken prisoners to Babylon ?
3. What four young men did Nebuchadnezzar choose to be his chosen pupils ?
4. How much better did the King consider these four than the others ?
5. What caused the King's spirit to be troubled ?
6. What did he do to try and get relief ?
7. Did he succeed in his endeavour ?
8. Who then was recommended to the King to help solve this problem ?

II.

9. What answer did Daniel give to the King ?
10. When the dream was explained, what did the King do ?
11. Who set up an immense image of gold, for worship ?
12. What penalty did the King make for disobedience of his command ?
13. Which three Jews, refusing to obey, were thrown into the furnace ?
14. What did the King say when he saw them unhurt by the flames ?
15. What other vision also interpreted by Daniel, did the King have ?
16. How was this vision actually fulfilled ?

III.

17. And what was the final result for the King ?
18. To how many of his Lords did Belshazzar give a feast ?
19. In the midst of the banquet, what appeared on the wall ?
20. Were any of the company able to understand the writing ?
21. Whom did the Queen suggest as being likely to know ?
22. What did Belshazzar say to Daniel ?
23. What was the interpretation of the strange writing ?
24. What happened that same night ?

MARY AND JOSEPH

I.

1. Where was Mary living when the birth of Jesus was foretold?
2. Which Angel brought the news to her?
3. What did Mary answer to the Angel's message?
4. The same Angel paid another visit to————whom?
5. What relation was Mary to Elizabeth, the mother of John?
6. Immediately after the Angel's appearance, whom did Mary go to visit?
7. Do you know the opening words of Mary's Magnificat?
8. In which town did Mary and Joseph live?

II.

9. Where did the Shepherds find Jesus, with Mary and Joseph?
10. And where did the Wise Men find them?
11. On how many occasions did an Angel appear to Joseph?
12. To which city did the holy family return from Egypt?
13. Twice we read " They were warned of God in a dream," who were " they "?
14. What prophecy did this specially fulfill?
15. What prophecy was fulfilled when they returned?
16. When Mary took Jesus to be circumcised, what two people met them?

III.

17. " The grace of God was upon Him "?
18. What did His parents do when Jesus was twelve?
19. What did Mary say to Jesus when they found Him in the Temple?
20. How many brethren had Jesus?
21. To whom did Jesus say " Behold thy Son "?
22. What were Mary's last recorded words?
23. On what occasion did Jesus' Mother and Brethren try to see Him?
24. Where do we last hear of Mary, the Mother of Jesus?

JAMES AND JOHN
I.
1. Which two brothers in a ship with their father, were called by Jesus ?
2. What were they doing, and what was their response ?
3. Do you know the name of their father ?
4. On what very special occasion did Jesus take them with Him ?
5. Both the brothers and one other disciple accompanied Jesus on a visit to———whom ?
6. Do we read that the brothers were present at the Crucifixion ?
7. On what occasion did the brothers greatly annoy the rest of the disciples ?
8. Both brothers asked Jesus a question "privately" we are told, what was it ?

II.
9. On what occasion were the brothers "astonished" at something ?
10. Immediately after the Ascension, where did James and and John live ?
11. Were the brothers present at Peter's sermon at Pentecost?
12. Which apostle was the first martyr ?
13. And who put him to death ?
14. Which two disciples were sent to prepare the Passove Feast ?
15. Which two disciples took part in the first miracle after the Ascension ?
16. The Sanhedrin marvelled at the boldness of which two disciples ?

III.
17. Who made the first Missionary Deputation ?
18. How many books of the Bible bear the name of John ?
19. To what disciple was the Revelation made ?
20. To whom did he specially write his Revelation ?
21. One of his letters is written to a lady and her children. Which ?
22. How did the two brothers wish to punish inhospitable villagers ?
23. Were the brother present when Jesus appeared at Tiberias after the Crucifixion ?
24. Who was 'the disciple whom Jesus loved '"?

SIMON PETER AND ANDREW

I.

1. Who were the first two brothers to be called by Jesus?
2. What did Jesus specially promise them?
3. Who else accompanied these two to the Transfiguration?
4. What special remark did one of them make?
5. Who also went with Jesus to the house of Jairus?
6. With what other two disciples did both once ask Jesus a private question?
7. What did Peter do and say after the miraculous draught of fishes?
8. What miracle did Jesus perform in the brother's home?

II.

9. Who was Jesus' first disciple?
10. And by whom was the second disciple brought to Jesus?
11. In which town did the two brothers live?
12. Which two disciples introduced a group of foreigners to Jesus?
13. Where are the two brothers living just before Pentecost?
14. Who introduced a lad to Jesus?
15. Why did Jesus once tell Peter to get behind Him?
16. When did Jesus instruct Peter to catch a fish?

III.

17. What caused Peter to remember the word of Jesus?
18. Whose ear did Peter cut off with a sword?
19. Why did a door remain closed to Peter, although they were so glad to see him?
20. When did Paul and Peter first meet?
21. When did Peter run a race with another apostle?
22. Who wrote "Casting all your care upon Him, for He careth for you"?
23. Was Andrew present at his brother's sermon at Pentecost?
24. What last commision did Jesus give to Peter?

PHILIP THE APOSTLE AND
PHILIP THE EVANGELIST

I.

1. To what city did Philip belong?
2. Who was it found Philip?
3. And who then did Philip find?
4. Who used the words " come and see " to a doubtful enquirer?
5. Who came to Philip saying " Sir, we would see Jesus "?
6. To whom did Philip pass on this request?
7. To whom did Jesus say " He that hath seen Me hath seen the Father "?
8. Was Philip present in the Upper Room before Pentecost?

II.

9. With whose name is Philip uniformly coupled in the Gospels?
10. Was Philip among those other disciples specially set apart for their office, first sent out by Christ?
11. Why did Jesus ask Philip "whence shall we buy bread "?
12. What great event did Philip see on the last time our Lord was seen on earth?
13. Is there another Philip mentioned in the Scriptures?
14. To which city was he the first to carry the Gospel outside Jerusalem?
15. Where was Philip next instructed to go?
16. Whom did he meet there?

III.

17. What conversation took place between them?
18. And what was the end of this encounter?
19. Which two cities did Philip next preach in?
20. What famous visitors once called at Philip's home?
21. How many?
22. How many others were chosen along with Philip the Evangelist as Deacons?
23. Who offered money that he might receive the Holy Spirit?
24. What reply was given to Him?

LUKE AND SILAS

I.

1. Which books of the New Testament did Luke write?
2. What was his profession?
3. For whom were his Epistles first written?
4. What special qualifications did Luke claim for writing his Gospel?
5. Is his name mentioned anywhere in his Gospel?
6. How many times does his name occur in the New Testament?
7. At what point in the book of Acts does he speak of himself?
8. Where does he next appear in company with Paul?

II.

9. With whom did he visit the Apostle James?
10. Was he with Paul on the memorable sea voyage and wreck?
11. Did he leave Paul when the Apostle was imprisoned in Rome?
12. What three other "fellow labourers" are mentioned with him by Paul?
13. On one occasion Paul was deserted, except by Luke, do you know the occasion?
14. In what city, so far as we are told, did Paul, Silas and Luke first meet?
15. Where are we first introduced to Silas?
16. Why do we conclude Luke was a Roman citizen?

III.

17. How many were chosen to go with Paul on his departure to Antioch?
18. Who did Paul choose to go with him on his second Missionary journey?
19. Can you name some of the towns they visited together?
20. Who were the first three Christian missionaries to visit Europe?
21. Who was their first convert?
22. And who was his second convert?
23. By what other name is he also referred to?
24. What adventure did he and Saul have in Phillipa?

PAUL AND BARNABAS

I.

1. What was Barnabas' other name, and what did it mean?
2. Where did Barnabas come from?
3. What is the first action we hear about him doing?
4. To what city was he first sent on a missionary journey?
5. What character does the writer of the Acts give Barnabas?
6. Where did he go to find Paul?
7. How long did the two men stay in Antioch?
8. During this time, the disciples of Jesus received a new name, what?

II.

9. The two were next sent on a mission to Jerusalem, for what reason?
10. On their return, they brought back with them a young man named ————?
11. Do you know any of the towns in Cyprus they visited?
12. Their next journey was to which district?
13. What was the name of the Roman Governor who was converted?
14. Somebody tried to upset the message of Paul and Barnabas, who?
15. What happened to this person?
16. Where was their next call after leaving Cyprus?

III.

17. After leaving the seaport they visited what three towns where very important things took place?
18. At what town were they mistaken for Roman Gods?
19. What was the outcome of this strange mistake?
20. What well-known Apostle took the chair when they addressed a meeting on their return to Jerusalem?
21. On their return, why did the two men separate and each go to a different area?
22. Each took an assistant. Who accompanied Paul?
23. And who went with Barnabas?
24. Who was the nephew of Barnabas?

TIMOTHY AND MARK

I.

1. What was the name of Timothy's mother?
2. And of his grandmother?
3. Was Timothy brought up as a Christian?
4. Do we gather from the Bible, that Timothy was a strong man?
5. From what district did Timothy come?
6. How did Paul often address him?
7. Timothy was told to do a certain work. What?
8. How do we know that Paul wished to encourage him in his studies?

II.

9. How many of Paul's letters to his young friend have been preserved?
10. From early life he was the constant companion of——who?
11. We read of Timothy accompanying Paul at many places. Name some.
12. Was Timothy ever imprisoned for his faith?
13. Do we ever read of Timothy crying?
14. What property of Paul's was he asked to forward to the Apostle?
15. What was Mark's surname?
16. What was the name of Mark's mother?

III.

17. To whom did he act as an assistant minister in Cyprus?
18. What apostles' service did he desert, to return home?
19. What apostle, on deliverance from prison, came to a prayer meeting at his mother's house?
20. However, at what episode did he again stand by the apostle's side?
21. With whom did he visit Babylon?
22. With whom did Mark go on a voyage to Cyprus?
23. Are Timothy and Mark mentioned together by Paul?
24. Mark's cousin was a well known disciple, who was he?

HEROD AND PONTIUS PILATE

I.

1. Which prophet did Herod execute ?
2. What happened on Herod's birthday ?
3. What was Pilate's famous question to Christ ?
4. Who was Pontius Pilate ?
5. Who mingled the blood of Galileans with their sacrifices ?
6. What was Pilate's first question of Jesus ?
7. Was Pilate aware of the reason why Jesus had been arrested ?
8. Whom did Pilate wish to release to the people ?

II.

9. Who did he finally release ?
10. What message did Pilate's wife send him ?
11. Why did Pilate deliver up Jesus to death ?
12. How did Jesus describe Herod ?
13. What two kinds of leaven did Jesus warn his disciples of ?
14. What did Joseph of Arimathaea beg of Pilate ?
15. What caused Herod to be perplexed ?
16. What did a deputation of Pharisees ask of Pilate ?

III.

17. And what was Pilate's reply ?
18. What was the occasion of Herod and Pilate becoming friends ?
19. What disciples did Herod put into prison ?
20. And which of these did he kill ?
21. Did Herod wish to see Jesus ?
22. What happened when he did see Jesus ?
23. Why did he specially want to see Christ ?
24. How did Herod die ?

JOHN THE BAPTIST AND HIS PARENTS

I.

1. What were the names of John the Baptist's parents ?
2. What were his father's duties ?
3. While engaged in his duties, what did he see ?
4. And what message was given to him ?
5. How did Zacharias receive the news ?
6. In what other way did the tidings affect him ?
7. Who visited Elizabeth soon after this ?
8. Who decided on John the Baptist's name ?

II.

9. When John commenced the Ministry, how did he describe himself ?
10. How was he clothed ?
11. And what was his food ?
12. What was his chief text of his sermons ?
13. How would you describe the Baptism of John ?
14. How did he liken himself to the Lord Jesus ?
15. What was his exclamation when he first saw Jesus ?
16. What did he say when Jesus came to be Baptised of him ?

III.

17. To whom did John say " Behold the Lamb of God "?
18. On what errand did John send two of his disciples to Jesus ?
19. How did Jesus describe John the Baptist ?
20. Who put John in prison ?
21. What was the outcome of Herod's foolish oath ?
22. When the superstitious Herod heard of Jesus' miracle, what did he say ?
23. Whom did John's disciples tell of this tragedy ?
24. When Jesus heard of this, what did he do ?

THE WOMEN WHO FOLLOWED JESUS

I.

1. What heathen woman came to Christ?
2. The mother of which two of his disciples came worshipping him?
3. To whose house did a woman bring an alabaster box of precious ointment for Christ?
4. What were the names of some of the women watching at the foot of the Cross?
5. What two women attended at the burial of Christ?
6. And which three women were first at the Tomb on Easter Day?
7. What did Simon's mother-in-law do as soon as Jesus had healed her?
8. On what occasion did his mother and brethren send to Him?

II.

9. To whom did our Lord appear first on Easter Day?
10. What women went with Christ on a preaching tour, and ministered to Him?
11. What woman, seeking healing, came behind Him?
12. What woman received Him into her house?
13. And what other woman, we read "sat at Jesus' feet"?
14. What did Jesus say to two sisters?
15. Which three women does Luke tell us announced the resurrection to the disciples?
16. Which woman was a guest at the Cana Wedding Feast?

III.

17. Which woman called her neighbours to see Jesus?
18. What woman wiped our Lord's feet with her hair?
19. Which two sisters do we read "Jesus loved"?
20. On what occasion did Jesus say " Behold, Thy Son"?
21. How many women named "Mary" waited at the foot of the Cross?
22. Which woman, on Easter Day came running to Simon Peter?
23. Who mistook Jesus for a gardener?
24. To whom did Jesus say " Touch me not"?

ROMAN CENTURIONS

I.

1. For whom did a Centurion beg our Lord's help?
2. What was Christ's commendation on him?
3. Give the verdict upon Christ of the Centurion who presided at the Crucifixion?
4. In what way did a Centurion show his regard for the Jewish religion?
5. Several Centurions are named in the Bible, who was specially concerned with Peter?
6. Of what legion was he the commander?
7. What were four points mentioned of his character?
8. What Centurion saw an earthquake?

II.

9. What was the outcome of the meeting with Peter?
10. By whom was Paul rescued during a Jewish riot?
11. Do we know this officer's name?
12. Who asked Paul if he could speak Greek?
13. Did he take Paul to be a Jew?
14. To whom did Paul's nephew tell a secret?
15. And what was this secret message?
16. What did the Roman commandant do to outwit this plot?

III.

17. What is the name of the centurion who was in charge of Paul to Rome?
18. What was his regiment?
19. How did he treat the apostle Paul?
20. Did the centurion believe Paul's warning of the impending shipwreck?
21. What was Paul's advice when the sailors began to lower a boat and escape?
22. Why did the Centurion Julius disregard the soldiers' counsel when the ship floundered?
23. To whom did the centurion deliver his prisoners when they finally reached Rome?
24. Who commanded a centurion to guard Paul, but to let him have liberty?

ANSWERS

to QUIZ No. 1

I.

1. Genesis 2: 8.
2. Genesis 2: 15.
3. Genesis 5: 2.
4. Genesis 2: 15.
5. Genesis 2: 20.
6. Genesis 2: 17.
7. Genesis 2: 17.
8. Genesis 2: 18.

II.

9. Genesis 3: 20.
10. Genesis 3: 1.
11. Genesis 3: 1.
12. Genesis 3: 2 and 3.
13. Genesis 3: 6.
14. Genesis 3: 8.
15. Genesis 3: 9.
16. Genesis 3: 12.

III.

17. Genesis 3: 21.
18. Genesis 3: 24.
19. Genesis 4: 1.
20. Genesis 4: 2.
21. 1 Corinthians 15: 47.
22. 1 Corinthians 15: 22.
23. Jude 14.
24. Revelation 22: 2.

to QUIZ No. 2

I.

1. Genesis 4: 1.
2. Genesis 4: 1.
3. Genesis 4: 2.
4. Genesis 4: 3.
5. Genesis 4: 5.
6. Genesis 4: 6 and 7.
7. Genesis 4: 5.
8. Genesis 4: 8.

II.

9. Genesis 4: 2.
10. Genesis 4: 2.
11. Genesis 4: 4.
12. Genesis 4: 4.
13. Hebrews 11: 4.
14. Genesis 4: 9.
15. Genesis 4: 9.
16. I John 3: 12.

III.

17. Genesis 4: 10-12.
18. Genesis 4: 13 and 14.
19. Genesis 4: 15.
20. Luke 11: 51.
21. Hebrews 12: 24.
22. Exodus 20: 13.
23. 1 John 3: 15.
24. Genesis 4: 25.

ANSWERS

to QUIZ No. 3

I.

1. Genesis 17: 5 and 15.
2. Genesis 11: 31 and 12: 1.
3. Genesis 11: 31.
4. Genesis 1:: 31 and 12: 4.
5. Genesis 12: 10.
6. Genesis 13: 7 and 9.
7. Genesis 12: 8, 13: 3, 13: 18, 20: 1, 21: 33.
8. Genesis 13: 14-17.

II.

9. Genesis 14: 14.
10. Genesis 14: 14 and 15.
11. Genesis 14: 19.
12. Genesis 17: 1.
13. Genesis 11: 31.
14. Genesis 12: 13 and 20: 5.
15. Genesis 18: 12 and 21: 6.
16. Genesis 17: 17.

III.

17. Genesis 21: 5.
18. Genesis 18: 14.
19. Genesis 18: 9-15.
20. 1 Peter 3: 6.
21. Hebrews 11: 11 and 31.
22. Luke 19: 9.
23. James 2: 23.
24. Romans 4: 1 and 23.

to QUIZ No. 4

I.

1. Genesis 16: 1.
2. Genesis 16: 6.
3. Genesis 16: 8.
4. Genesis 16: 11.
5. Genesis 16: 13.
6. Genesis 16: 15.
7. Genesis 17: 18.
8. Genesis 17: 20.

II.

9. Genesis 21: 9.
10. Genesis 21: 10.
11. Genesis 21: 11.
12. Genesis 21: 12.
13. Genesis 21: 14.
14. Genesis 21: 14.
15. Genesis 21: 14.
16. Genesis 21: 15.

III.

17. Genesis 21: 16.
18. Genesis 21: 17.
19. Genesis 21: 17.
20. Genesis 21: 19.
21. Genesis 21: 19.
22. Galatians 4: 25.
23. Galatians 4: 22-24.
24. Genesis 25: 9.

ANSWERS

to QUIZ No. 5

I.

1. Genesis 11: 27.
2. Genesis 12: 4.
3. Genesis 13: 6 and 8.
4. Genesis 13: 9.
5. Genesis 13: 12.
6. Genesis 14: 12 and 16.
7. Genesis 19: 13 and 24.
8. Genesis 19: 16 and 26.

II.

9. Luke 17: 28 and 32.
10. II Peter 2: 6 and 7.
11. Genesis 19: 26.
12. Genesis 19: 1 and 13.
13. Genesis 24: 29.
14. Genesis 24: 29.
15. Genesis 24: 31.
16. Genesis 24: 3.

III.

17. Genesis 27: 43.
18. Genesis 29: 13.
19. Genesis 29: 15.
20. Genesis 29: 26 and 27.
21. Genesis 31: 27.
22. Genesis 31: 41.
23. Genesis 31: 48 and 49.
24. Genesis 31: 55.

to QUIZ No. 6

I.

1. Genesis 17: 19.
2. Genesis 22: 2.
3. Genesis 22: 2.
4. Genesis 22: 11 and 12.
5. Genesis 24: 4.
6. Genesis 24: 15.
7. Genesis 24: 58.
8. Genesis 24: 64.

II.

9. Genesis 24: 64.
10. Genesis 24: 63.
11. Genesis 26: 12-16. 18-19.
12. Genesis 26: 12-14.
13. Genesis 26: 28.
14. Genesis 25: 27.
15. Genesis 35: 8.
16. Genesis 27: 3 and 4.

III.

17. Genesis 27: 26-30.
18. Genesis 27: 43.
19. Genesis 27: 44.
20. Genesis 35: 29.
21. Genesis 33: 4.
22. Romans 9: 10.
23. Matthew 8: 11. Luke 13: 28.
24. Genesis 21: 12. Romans 9: 7. Hebrews 11: 18.

ANSWERS

to QUIZ No. 7

I.

1. Genesis 25: 27.
2. Genesis 25: 28.
3. Genesis 25: 30-33.
4. Genesis 27: 3 and 4.
5. Genesis 27: 5 and 10.
6. Genesis 27: 16.
7. Genesis 27: 8-10.
8. Genesis 27: 23.

II.

9. Genesis 27: 30-35.
10. Genesis 27: 42 and 43.
11. Genesis 28: 2.
12. John 4: 6.
13. Hebrews 12: 16.
14. Genesis 28: 12.
15. Genesis 31: 41.
16. Genesis 28: 13-15.

III.

17. Genesis 28: 12. 32: 1.
18. Genesis 32: 24-30.
19. Genesis 32. 28.
20. Genesis 35: 22.
21. Genesis 37: 3 and 44: 20.
22. Genesis 48: 16.
23. I Kings 18: 31.
24. Genesis 47: 10.

to QUIZ No. 8

I.

1. Genesis 30: 24.
2. Genesis 33: 2.
3. Genesis 37: 2.
4. Genesis 37: 3.
5. Genesis 37: 3.
6. Genesis 37: 4.
7. Genesis 37: 5-9.
8. Genesis 37: 10.

II.

9. Genesis 37: 12-14.
10. Genesis 37: 15-17.
11. Genesis 37: 20-22.
12. Genesis 37. 24.
13. Genesis 37: 27 and 28.
14. Genesis 37: 36.
15. Genesis 39: 2-4.
16. Genesis 40: 9-11. 16-18.

III.

17. Genesis 41: 37-43.
18. Genesis 42: 34.
19. Genesis 42: 36 and 38.
20. Genesis 43: 29.
21. Genesis 43: 34.
22. Genesis 49: 22 and 27.
23. Genesis 49: 27.
24. Acts 7: 9. 12-14.

ANSWERS

I.

1. Exodus 2: 4 and Numbers 26: 59.
2. Exodus 4: 14 and 15.
3. Numbers 12: 3.
4. Exodus 2: 15.
5. Exodus 4: 27.
6. Exodus 4: 29-31.
7. Exodus 5: 1.
8. Exodus 7: 1.

II.

9. Exodus 7: 7.
10. Exodus 7: 12 and Numbers 17: 7 and 8.
11. Exodus 8: 6.
12. Exodus 12: 31.
13. Exodus 16: 2 and 3.
14. Exodus 16: 6, 9, 14, 15.
15. Exodus 17: 10-12.
16. Exodus 19: 24.

III.

17. Exodus 32: 1-6.
18. Exodus 32: 23 and 24.
19. Exodus 28: 1 and Numbers 8: 11.
20. Deuteronomy 9: 20.
21. Numbers 20: 27-29 and Deuteronomy 34: 1 and 5.
22. Acts 7: 37.
23. Hebrews 3: 2.
24. John 3: 14 and 15.

I.

1. Exodus 2: 10.
2. Exodus 2: 15.
3. Exodus 1: 8.
4. Exodus 4: 19.
5. Exodus 5: 2.
6. Exodus 5: 7-9.
7. Exodus 7 to 11.
8. Exodus 12: 29.

II.

9. Exodus 14: 5.
10. Exodus 14: 10-12.
11. Exodus 14: 23.
12. Exodus 14: 28.
13. Exodus 2: 18.
14. Exodus 2: 15.
15. Exodus 2: 16.
16. Genesis 24: 14. 29: 10, 18 and Exodus 2: 19-21.

III.

17. Exodus 3: 1.
18. Acts 7: 23, 29 and 30.
19. Exodus 3: 1.
20. Exodus 4: 18.
21. Exodus 18: 5 and 6.
22. Exodus 18: 17-23.
23. Numbers 10: 29.
24. Romans 9: 17.

ANSWERS

to QUIZ No. 11

I.

1. Exodus 17: 9.
2. Exodus 24: 13 and Joshua 1: 1.
3. Exodus 32: 17.
4. Exodus 33: 11.
5. Numbers 13: 2 and 8.
6. Numbers 13: 6.
7. Numbers 14: 30.
8. Deuteronomy 1: 36 and 38.

II.

9. Numbers 27: 18.
10. Numbers 34: 17.
11. Deuteronomy 1: 38 and 3: 28.
12. Deuteronomy 34: 9.
13. Joshua 1:6 and 18.
14. Joshua 2: 1.
15. Joshua 4: 3 and 8.
16. Joshua 5: 13 and 6: 1.

III.

17. Joshua 14: 10 and 14.
18. Joshua 15: 18 and 19.
19. Joshua 6: 3 and 4.
20. Joshua 7: 4 and 5.
21. Joshua 10: 12.
22. Joshua 13: 1.
23. Joshua 18: 8-10.
24. Joshua 24: 15.

to QUIZ No. 12

I.

1. Judges 6: 1.
2. Judges 6: 1.
3. Judges 6: 6.
4. Judges 6: 11.
5. Judges 6: 11.
6. Judges 6: 12.
7. Judges 6: 14.
8. Judges 6: 19 and 20.

II.

9. Judges 6: 21-24.
10. Judges 6: 25 and 27.
11. Judges 7: 2-6.
12. Judges 7: 19.
13. Judges 13: 2.
14. Judges 13: 3.
15. Judges 14: 5 and 6.
16. Judges 14: 14 and 18.

III.

17. Judges 15: 4 and 5.
18. Judges 16: 2 and 3.
19. Judges 16: 18.
20. Judges 16: 20 and 21.
21. Judges 16: 26-30.
22. Judges 16: 6.
23. Hebrews 11: 32.
24. Hebrews 11: 32.

ANSWERS

to QUIZ No. 13

I.

1. Ruth.
2. Ruth 1: 4.
3. Ruth 1: 8.
4. Ruth 1: 6.
5. Ruth 1: 14.
6. Ruth 1: 16 and 17.
7. Ruth 1. 19.
8. Ruth 1: 22.

II.

9. Ruth 2: 2.
10. Ruth 2: 3.
11. Ruth 2: 8.
12. Ruth 2: 15 and 16.
13. Ruth 3: 16 and 17.
14. Ruth 4: 7 and 8.
15. Ruth 4: 3 and 9.
16. Ruth 4: 13.

III.

17. Ruth 4: 16.
18. Ruth 4: 17.
19. Ruth 4: 17.
20. Matthew 1: 5.
21. Ruth 1: 16.
22. Ruth 1: 4.
23. Ruth 1: 21.
24. Ruth 2: 12.

to QUIZ No. 14

I.

1. I Samuel 1: 1.
2. I Samuel 1: 3.
3. I Samuel 1: 3.
4. I Samuel 1: 9.
5. I Samuel 1: 11.
6. I Samuel 1: 13 and 18.
7. I Samuel 1: 19.
8. I Samuel 1: 20.

II.

9. I Samuel 1: 28.
10. I Samuel 2: 1-10.
11. I Samuel 2: 11.
12. I Samuel 2: 18.
13. I Samuel 2: 19.
14. I Samuel 2: 26 and Luke 2: 52.
15. I Samuel 2: 27 and 34.
16. I Samuel 3: 1-3.

III.

17. I Samuel 3: 5.
18. I Samuel 3: 8.
19. I Samuel 3: 8.
20. I Samuel 3: 9.
21. I Samuel 3: 13.
22. I Samuel 3: 15.
23. I Samuel 3: 18.
24. I Samuel 4: 15-18.

ANSWERS

to QUIZ No. 15

I.

1. I Samuel 13: 2.
2. I Samuel 13: 22.
3. I Samuel 14: 1.
4. I Samuel 14: 28-44.
5. I Samuel 14: 45.
6. I Samuel 10: 23.
7. I Samuel 10: 24.
8. I Samuel 17: 38 and 39.

II.

9. I Samuel 18: 1.
10. I Samuel 19: 13 and 14.
11. I Samuel 20: 17.
12. I Samuel 20: 33. 18: 11 and 19: 10.
13. I Samuel 20: 20.
14. I Samuel 24: 10. 26: 7-11.
15. I Samuel 26: 21.
16. I Samuel 28: 7.

III.

17. I Samuel 28: 19.
18. I Samuel 31: 2.
19. II Samuel 1: 23.
20. I Samuel 9: 2.
21. I Samuel 26: 21.
22. I Samuel 20: 16.
23. Acts 26: 19.
24. Acts 7: 58.

to QUIZ No. 16

I.

1. II Samuel 13: 1.
2. II Samuel 14: 25.
3. II Samuel 14: 26.
4. II Samuel 14: 28.
5. II Samuel 14: 31.
6. II Samuel 15: 1.
7. II Samuel 15: 2-5.
8. II Samuel 15: 6.

II.

9. II Samuel 15: 8.
10. II Samuel 15: 10.
11. II Samuel 15: 14.
12. II Samuel 15: 23.
13. II Samuel 15: 31.
14. II Samuel 16: 13.
15. II Samuel 17: 2.
16. II Samuel 17: 13.

III.

17. II Samuel 18: 5.
18. II Samuel 18: 6.
19. II Samuel 18: 9.
20. II Samuel 18: 10-13.
21. II Samuel 18: 17.
22. II Samuel 18: 24-28.
23. II Samuel 18: 29 and 32.
24. II Samuel 18: 33.

ANSWERS

to QUIZ No. 17

I.

1. II Samuel 5: 11.
2. II Samuel 5: 11.
3. I Kings 5: 1.
4. I Kings 5: 5.
5. I Kings 5: 9.
6. I Kings 5: 11.
7. I Kings 5: 18.
8. I Kings 6: 1.

II.

9. I Kings 6: 38.
10. I Kings 7: 14.
11. I Kings 7: 21.
12. I Kings 8: 9.
13. I Kings 8: 30, 32, 34, 36, 39, 43, 45, 49.
14. I Kings 3: 5 and 9: 2.
15. I Kings 9: 11.
16. I Kings 9: 26.

III.

17. I Kings 10: 1.
18. I Kings 10: 1.
19. I Kings 5: 1.
20. I Kings 10: 28.
21. I Kings 10: 26.
22. I Kings 3: 9.
23. II Samuel 12: 24.
24. I Kings 4: 29. 5: 12.
    II Chronicles 1: 12.

to QUIZ No. 18

I.

1. I Kings 11: 26.
2. I Kings 11: 28.
3. I Kings 11: 29-31.
4. I Kings 11: 40.
5. I Kings 11: 40.
6. I Kings 12: 20.
7. I King 12: 20.
8. I Kings 12: 20.

II.

9. I Kings 12: 27.
10. I Kings 12: 28.
11. I Kings 12: 29.
12. I Kings 12: 30.
13. I Kings 13: 2.
14. I Kings 13: 3.
15. I Kings 13: 4.
16. I Kings 13: 6.

III.

17. I Kings 13: 7-9.
18. I Kings 13: 11-32.
19. I Kings 14: 1.
20. I Kings 14: 2 and 3.
21. I Kings 14: 4 and 5.
22. I Kings 14: 6.
23. I Kings 14: 12.
24. I Kings 14: 13.

ANSWERS

to QUIZ No. 19

I.

1. I Kings 16: 29.
2. I Kings 16: 30.
3. I Kings 16: 31.
4. I Kings 16: 31.
5. I Kings 17: 1.
6. I Kings 18: 1.
7. I Kings 19: 2.
8. I Kings 21: 1.

II.

9. I Kings 21: 1.
10. I Kings 21: 2.
11. I Kings 21: 3.
12. I Kings 21: 4.
13. I Kings 21: 5.
14. I Kings 21: 7.
15. I Kings 21: 8-10.
16. I Kings 21: 11-14.

III.

17. I Kings 21: 15-16.
18. I Kings 21: 17-18.
19. I Kings 21: 20.
20. I Kings 21: 23.
21. I Kings 21: 27-29.
22. I Kings 22: 6 and 14.
23. I Kings 22: 30.
24. I Kings 22: 31 and 34.

to QUIZ No. 20

I.

1. I Kings 18: 3.
2. I Kings 18: 4.
3. I Kings 18: 5-6.
4. I Kings 18: 7.
5. I Kings 18: 8.
6. I Kings 18: 9-14.
7. I Kings 18: 15.
8. James 5: 17.

II.

9. I Kings 18: 17-18.
10. I Kings 18: 19.
11. I Kings 18: 19.
12. I Kings 18: 21.
13. I Kings 18: 21.
14. I Kings 19: 6.
15. I Kings 17: 1.
16. I Kings 19: 19.

III.

17. I Kings 18: 39.
18. I Kings 17: 3.
19. I Kings 17: 9.
20. I Kings 17: 9.
21. I Kings 17: 16-22.
22. I Kings 19: 7.
23. II Kings 2: 4.
24. II Kings 2: 11.

ANSWERS

to QUIZ No. 21

I.

1. II Chronicles 14: 2.
   I Kings 15: 11.
2. I Kings 15: 13.
3. II Chronicles 14: 11.
4. II Chronicles 15: 7.
5. II Chronicles 15: 12.
6. II Chronicles 16: 13.
7. I Kings 13: 2.
8. II Kings 22: 1.

II.

9. II Kings 22: 2.
10. II Chronicles 34: 1.
11. II Chronicles 34: 3.
12. II Chronicles 34: 8.
13. II Chronicles 34: 14.
14. II Chronicles 34: 18.
15. II Chronicles 34: 21.
16. II Chronicles 34: 28.

III.

17. II Kings 23: 22-23.
18. II Kings 23: 25.
19. II Chronicles 35: 20-23.
20. II Chronicles 35: 25.
21. Jeremiah 1: 2.
22. Zephaniah 1: 1.
23. II Chronicles 34: 33.
24. II Chronicles 35: 25-26.

to QUIZ No. 22

I.

1. Esther.
2. Esther 1: 1.
3. Esther 1: 1.
4. Esther 1: 1.
5. Esther 1: 9.
6. Esther 1: 12.
7. Esther 1: 19.
8. Esther 2: 5.

II.

9. Esther 2: 7.
10. Esther 2: 17.
11. Esther 2: 21-23.
12. Esther 3: 2.
13. Esther 3: 6.
14. Esther 3: 8-11.
15. Esther 4: 1, 7 and 8.
16. Esther 4: 16.

III.

17. Esther 5: 4.
18. Esther 5: 14.
19. Esther 7: 4 and 6.
20. Esther 7: 9 and 10.
21. Esther 8: 2 and 8.
22. Esther 8: 9.
23. Esther 3: 13 and 8: 10.
24. Esther 8: 15.

ANSWERS

to QUIZ No. 23

I.

1. II Kings 16: 20.
2. II Kings 18: 2.
3. II Kings 18: 2.
4. II Kings 18: 4.
5. II Chronicles 29: 3.
6. II Chronicles 29: 17.
7. II Chronicles 29: 36.
8. II Chronicles 30: 6.

II.

9. II Chronicles 30: 10.
10. II Chronicles 30: 18.
11. II Chronicles 32: 1.
12. II Chronicles 32: 3 and 4.
13. II Chronicles 32: 7 and 8.
14. II Chronicles 32: 10-13.
15. II Chronicles 32: 18 and 19.
16. II Kings 18: 26.

III.

17. II Kings 18: 19.
18. II Kings 19: 14 and 15.
19. II Chronicles 32: 20.
20. II Kings 19: 20.
21. II Kings 19: 35.
22. II Kings 20: 1.
23. II Kings 20: 6.
24. II Kings 20: 7 and 11.

to QUIZ No. 24

I.

1. Ezra 1: 2.
2. Ezra 1: 5.
3. Ezra 3: 12-13.
4. Ezra 4: 16 and 21.
5. Ezra 5: 2.
6. Ezra 7: 6.
7. Ezra 7: 10.
8. Ezra 7: 11-13.

II.

9. Ezra 8: 22.
10. Ezra 8: 31.
11. Ezra 10: 9.
12. Nehemiah 1: 11.
13. Nehemiah 1: 3 and 4.
14. Nehemiah 2: 2.
15. Nehemiah 2: 5.
16. Nehemiah 2: 6.

III.

17. Nehemiah 2: 11 and 12.
18. Nehemiah 2: 17.
19. Nehemiah 4: 1.
20. Nehemiah 4: 16 and 21.
21. Nehemiah 4: 19 and 20.
22. Nehemiah 5: 17.
23. Nehemiah 8: 3 and 4.
24. Nehemiah 8: 10.

ANSWERS

to QUIZ No. 25

I.

1. II Kings 24: 1.
2. II Kings 24: 11 and 12.
3. Daniel 1: 6.
4. Daniel 1: 20.
5. Daniel 2: 1.
6. Daniel 2: 3-5.
7. Daniel 2: 11.
8. Daniel 2: 25.

II.

9. Daniel 2: 27 and 28.
10. Daniel 2: 46.
11. Daniel 3: 1.
12. Daniel 3: 6.
13. Daniel 3: 19.
14. Daniel 3: 28.
15. Daniel 4: 9-12.
16. Daniel 4: 34.

III.

17. Daniel 4: 37.
18. Daniel 5: 1.
19. Daniel 5: 5.
20. Daniel 5: 8.
21. Daniel 5 :11 and 12.
22. Daniel 5: 13 and 14.
23. Daniel 5: 25-28.
24. Daniel 5: 30.

to QUIZ No. 26

I.

1. Luke 1: 26.
2. Luke 1: 26.
3. Luke 1: 38.
4. Luke 1: 18 and 19.
5. Luke 1: 36.
6. Luke 1: 39 and 40.
7. Luke 1: 46.
8. Luke 2: 4.

II.

9. Luke 2: 16.
10. Matthew 2: 11.
11. Matthew 1: 20. 2: 13. 2: 19.
12. Matthew 2: 23.
13. Matthew 2: 12 and 2: 22.
14. Matthew 2: 15.
15. Matthew 2: 23.
16. Luke 2: 25 and 36.

III.

17. Luke 2: 40.
18. Luke 2: 42.
19. Luke 2: 48.
20. Matthew 13: 55.
21. John 19: 27.
22. John 2: 5.
23. Matthew 12: 46.
24. Acts 1: 14.

ANSWERS

to QUIZ No. 27

I.
1. Matthew 4: 21.
2. Matthew 4: 21 and 22.
3. Matthew 4: 21.
4. Matthew 17: 1.
5. Mark 5: 37.
6. NO.
7. Mark 10: 35-41.
8. Mark 13: 3 and 4.

II.
9. Luke 5: 9and 10.
10. Acts 1: 13.
11. Acts 2: 14.
12. Acts 12: 2.
13. Acts 12: 2.
14. Luke 22: 8.
15. Acts 3: 1-6.
16. Acts 4: 13.

III.
17. Acts 8: 14.
18. The Gospel of John ;
    John 1: 2 and 3.
19. Revelation 1: 1.
20. Revelation 1: 4.
21. John 2.
22. Luke 9: 54.
23. John 21: 2.
24. John 21: 7.

to QUIZ No. 28

I.
1. Matthew 4: 18.
2. Matthew 4: 19.
3. Matthew 17: 1.
4. Matthew 17: 4.
5. Mark 5: 37.
6. Mark 13: 3 and 4.
7. Luke 5: 8.
8. Mark 1: 29-31.

II.
9. John 1: 40.
10. John 1: 41.
11. John 1: 44.
12. John 12: 21 and 22.
13. Acts 1: 13.
14. John 6: 9.
15. Matthew 16: 23.
16. Matthew 17: 27.

III.
17. Matthew 26: 75.
18. John 18: 10.
19. Acts 12: 14.
20. Galations 1: 18.
21. John 20: 4.
22. I Peter 5: 7.
23. Acts 2: 14.
24. John 21: 19.

ANSWERS

<table>
<tr><td>

to QUIZ No. 29

I.

1. John 1: 44.
2. John 1: 43.
3. John 1: 45.
4. John 1: 46.
5. John 12: 21.
6. John 12: 22.
7. John 14: 9.
8. Acts 1: 13.

II.

9. Matthew 10: 3.
   Mark 3: 18.
   Luke 6: 14.
10. Matthew 10: 1 and 3.
11. John 6: 6.
12. Acts 1: 13.
13. Acts 6: 5.
14. Acts 8: 5.
15. Acts 8: 26.
16. Acts 8: 27.

III.

17. Acts 8: 29-31.
18. Acts 8: 36-39.
19. Acts 8: 40.
20. Acts 21: 8.
21. Acts 21: 8.
22. Acts 6: 5.
23. Acts 8: 18.
24. Acts 8: 20.

</td><td>

to QUIZ No. 30

I.

1. Luke 1: 1 and Acts 1: 1.
2. Colossians 4: 14.
3. Luke 1: 3 and Acts 1: 1.
4. Luke 1: 3.
5. NO.
6. Colossians 4: 14.
   II Timothy 4: 11.
   Philemon 24.
7. Acts 16: 10.
8. Acts 20: 6.

II.

9. Acts 21: 18.
10. Acts 27: 2.
11. Colossians 4: 14.
12. Philemon 24.
13. II Timothy 4: 11.
14. Acts 16: 12 and 19.
15. Acts 15: 22.
16. Acts 16: 37.

III.

17. Acts 15: 22.
18. Acts 15: 40.
19. Acts 16: 1, 7 and 9.
20. Acts 16: 12 and 19.
21. Acts 16: 14.
    II Corinthians 1: 19.
22. Acts 16: 30.
23. II Corinthians 1: 19.
    I Thessalonians 1: 1.
    II Thessalonians 1: 1.
24. Acts 16: 19-24.

</td></tr>
</table>

ANSWERS

to QUIZ No. 31

I.
1. Acts 4: 36.
2. Acts 4: 36.
3. Acts 4: 37.
4. Acts II: 22.
5. Acts 11: 24.
6. Acts 11: 25.
7. Acts 11: 26.
8. Acts 11: 26.

II.
9. Acts 11: 29 and 30.
10. Acts 12: 25.
11. Acts 13: 5 and 6.
12. Acts 13: 4.
13. Acts 13: 7.
14. Acts 13: 8.
15. Acts 13: 11.
16. Acts 13: 14.

III.
17. Acts 14: 1, 6 and 8.
18. Acts 14: 8-13.
19. Acts 14: 19 and 20.
20. Acts 15: 12 and 13.
21. Acts 15: 36-39.
22. Acts 15: 40 and 41.
23. Acts 15: 39.
24. Colossians 4: 10.

to QUIZ No. 32

I.
1. II Timothy 1: 5.
2. II Timothy 1: 5.
3. II Timothy 3: 15.
4. I Timothy 5: 23.
5. Acts 16: 1 and 2.
6. I Timothy 1: 18.
   I Timothy 1: 2.
   II Timothy 1: 2.
7. II Timothy 4: 5.
8. I Timothy 4: 14.

II.
9. I Timothy and II Timothy.
10. I Corinthians 4: 17.
11. Acts 16: 12.
    Acts 17: 14.
    I Thessalonians 3: 2.
    I Thessalonians 1: 1.
    II Thessalonians 1: 1.
    Acts 19: 22.
12. Hebrews 13: 23.
13. II Timothy 1: 4.
14. II Timothy 4: 13.
15. Acts 12: 12.
16. Acts 12: 12.

III.
17. Acts 15: 39.
18. Acts 13: 13.
19. Acts 12: 12.
20. Colossians 4: 10.
21. I Peter 5: 13.
22. Acts 15: 39.
23. II Timothy 4: 11.
24. Colossians 4: 10.

ANSWERS

I.
1. Matthew 14: 10.
2. Mark 6: 21.
3. John 18: 38.
4. Matthew 27: 2.
5. Luke 13: 1.
6. Matthew 27: 11.
7. Matthew 27: 18.
8. Luke 23: 20.

II.
9. Matthew 27: 26.
10. Matthew 27: 19.
11. Mark 15: 15.
12. Luke 13: 32.
13. Mark 8: 15.
14. Matthew 27: 58.
15. Luke 9: 7.
16. Matthew 27: 64.

III.
17. Matthew 27: 65.
18. Luke 23: 12.
19. Acts 12: 2 and 3.
20. Acts 12: 2.
21. Luke 9: 9.
22. Luke 23: 9.
23. Luke 23: 8.
24. Acts 12: 21 and 23.

I.
1. Luke 1: 5.
2. Luke 1: 8 and 9.
3. Luke 1: 11.
4. Luke 1: 13.
5. Luke 1: 20.
6. Luke 1: 22.
7. Luke 1: 39 and 40.
8. Luke 1: 13.

II.
9. Matthew 3: 3.
   Mark 1: 3.
   Luke 3: 4.
10. Matthew 3: 4.
11. Mark 1: 6.
12. Matthew 3: 3.
    Mark 1: 3.
13. Luke 3: 4.
    Matthew 3: 11.
    Mark 1: 8.
14. Matthew 3: 11.
    Mark 1: 7.
15. John 1: 29.
16. Mathew 3: 14.

III.
17. John 1: 35-40.
18. Matthew 11: 3.
19. Luke 7: 28.
20. Matthew 14: 3.
21. Matthew 14: 9.
22. Matthew 14: 2.
23. Matthew 14: 12.
24. Matthew 14: 13 and 14.

ANSWERS

I.

1. Mark 7: 25.
   Matthew 15: 22.
2. Matthew 20: 20.
3. Matthew 26: 7.
4. Matthew 27: 56.
   Mark 15: 40.
5. Mark 15: 47.
   Matthew 27: 56.
6. Matthew 28: 1.
   Mark 16: 1.
7. Mark 1: 31.
8. Mark 3: 31-35.

II.

9. Mark 16: 9.
10. Luke 8: 1-3.
11. Luke 8: 43 and 44.
12. Luke 10: 38.
13. Luke 10: 39.
14. Luke 10: 40-42.
15. Luke 24: 10.
16. John 2: 1.

III.

17. John 4: 29.
18. John 11: 2.
19. John 11: 5.
20. John 19: 26.
21. John 19: 25.
22. John 20: 1.
23. John 20: 15.
24. John 20: 17.

I.

1. Mathew 8: 6.
2. Matthew 8: 10.
3. Matthew 27: 54.
4. Luke 7: 5.
5. Acts 10: 1.
6. Acts 10: 1.
7. Acts 10: 2.
8. Matthew 27: 54.

II.

9. Acts 10: 44-48.
10. Acts 21: 32.
11. Acts 24: 7.
12. Acts 21: 37.
13. Acts 21: 38.
14. Acts 23: 17.
15. Acts 23: 20 and 21.
16. Acts 23: 23 and 24.

III.

17. Acts 27: 1.
18. Acts 27: 1.
19. Acts 27: 3.
20. Acts 27: 11.
21. Acts 27: 31.
22. Acts 27: 43.
23. Acts 28: 16.
24. Acts 24: 22 and 23.